ON DUTY!
ACTIVITY BOOK

These people all have different vehicles.

Draw lines to match each person with the vehicle they use.

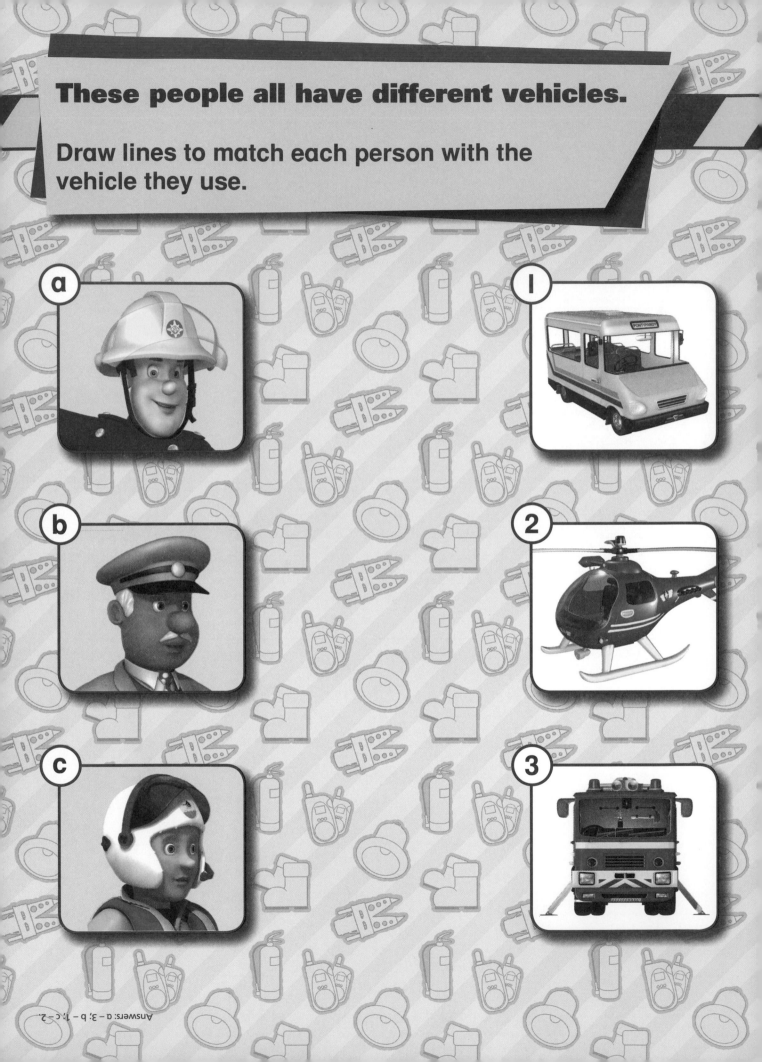

a

b

c

1

2

3

Give the thumbs up to Sam, the hero next door!

Colour in the big picture of Fireman Sam, using the smaller one to help you.

Fireman Sam is checking Jupiter's equipment.

How many of each thing can you count in the big picture?
Write the numbers in the boxes.

These pictures of Jupiter may look the same, but one is different.

Can you spot the odd one out?

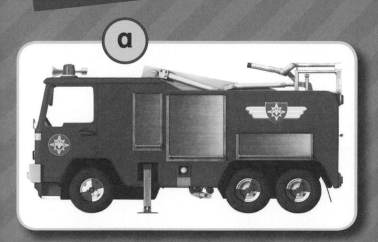

a

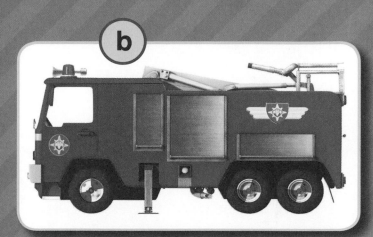

b

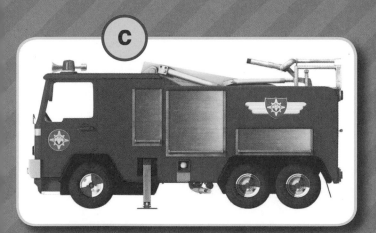

c

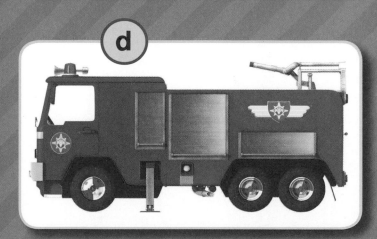

d

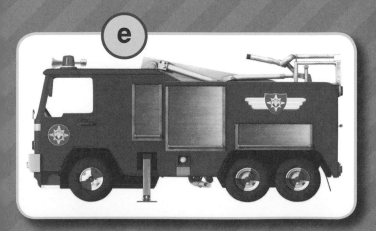

e

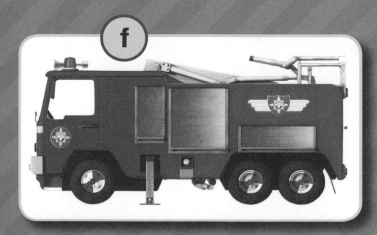

f

Station Officer Steele has lost his buttons!

Draw over the grey lines to add 8 shiny buttons to his uniform, then colour in the picture.

Lots of people live in Pontypandy!

Do you know their names? Put a tick (✓) next to the picture of the person whose name is in the box.

Sam
a b c

Norman
a b c

Penny
a b c

Mandy needs to find her friend, Norman.

Which path should she take to reach him?

a →

b →

c →

Colour in this picture of Sarah and James getting ready to go skateboarding.

These pictures of Sam look the same but 5 things are different in picture 2.

1

Can you spot them all?
Draw a circle around each difference you find.

②

Sam and Elvis are practising for an emergency.

How many of each thing can you count in the picture? Write the numbers in the boxes.

helmets ⬭

hose ⬭

boots ⬭

Now colour in this picture of Fireman Sam and Elvis Cridlington.

You can use the picture opposite to help you, or choose your own colours.

These little pictures can all be found in the big picture, opposite.

Tick the circles when you've found them, then colour in the big picture.

Sam has just heard about an emergency!

What do you think Fireman Sam would say?

a. "Great Fires of Newcastle!"

b. "Great Fires of London!"

c. "Great Fires of Cornwall!"

d. "Great Fires of Kent!"

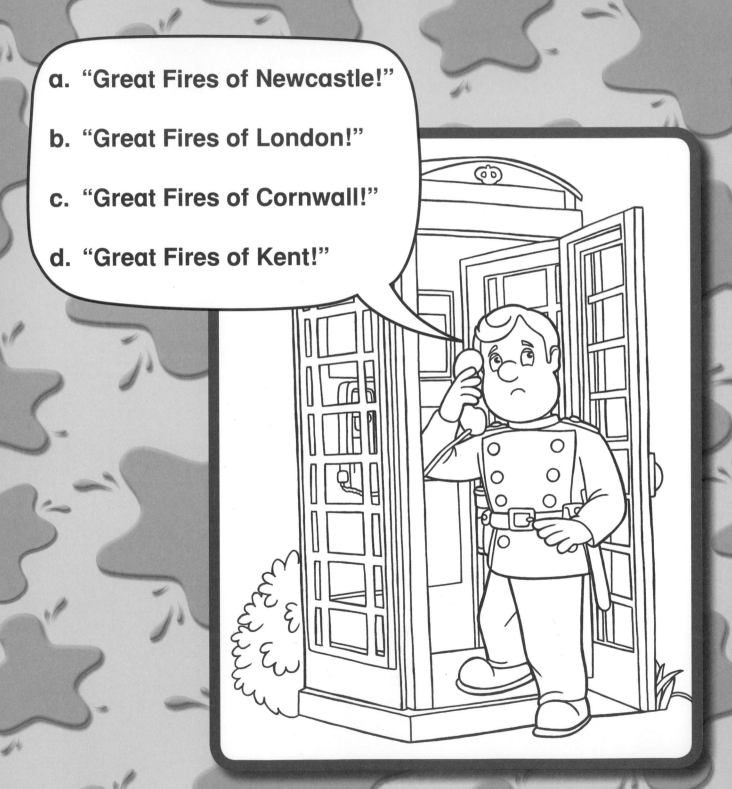

Draw lines to match Sam's friends to the right names.

a Station Officer Steele

b Norman

c Penny

d Tom

e Elvis

Can you work out who or what these close-up pictures are of?

a

b

_____

_____

c

d

_____

_____

Look at this picture for 60 seconds. When the time is up, cover the picture and try to answer the questions below.

① **Who is holding Lion?**
a. Penny   b. Bronwyn   c. Sam

② **Who is wearing a hat?**
a. Charlie   b. Station Officer Steele   c. Tom

③ **What picture is on the wall?**
a. a tree   b. a bottle   c. a cup of tea and 2 fish.

How many times can you find Sam in the picture below?

I found Sam ☐ times.

Who wants to reach the Fire Station?
Who wants to catch the bus?
Who wants to go for a country walk?

Follow the paths to find out.

These pictures of Norman look the same but one of them is different from the rest.

Can you spot the odd one out?

Answer: picture e is the odd one out – there is no pattern on his trousers.

How well do you know Fireman Sam and his friends?

Answer the questions below by circling the correct answer.

1 Where does Fireman Sam live?

a. Pontypandy   b. Pontypokey   c. Pontyparsley

2 What is the name of Sam's chief officer?

a. Officer Iron   b. Station Officer Steele   c. Officer Brass

3 What kind of animal is Radar?

a. a dog   b. a rabbit   c. a cow

4 What does Charlie sell in his shop?

a. wool   b. clothes   c. fish

5 What colour is Sam's fireman's helmet?

a. yellow   b. red   c. blue

I scored [ ] out of 5!